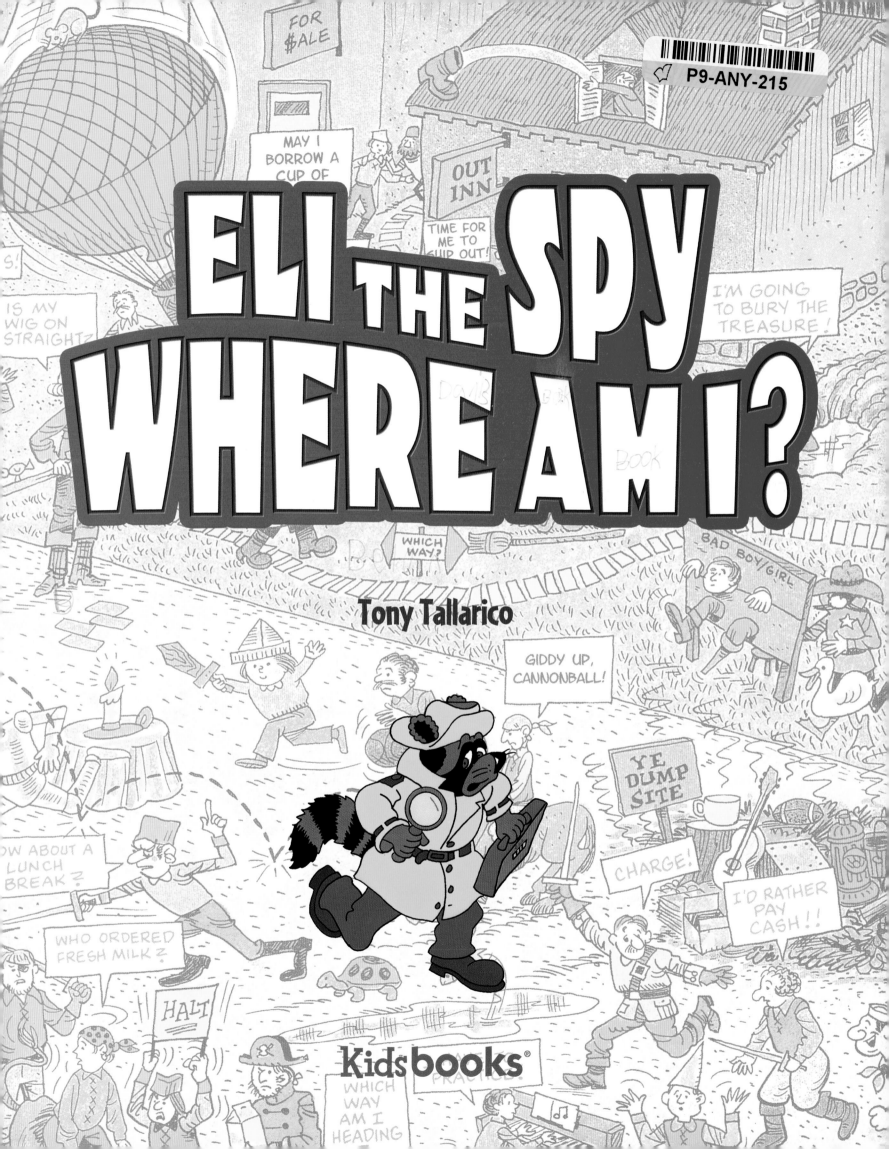

Visit us at **www.kidsbooks.com**®

INTRODUCTION

Poor Eli the Spy doesn't have a clue, but that won't stop him from cracking this mysterious case. Youngsters will have fun with him as he stumbles through one wacky place after another, trying to figure out where he is. Early readers will love to help Eli search for clues and find all the fun objects hidden in each exciting scene.

Read, Search & Find® books help sharpen a child's reading, concentration, and cognitive skills. The careful searching for hidden objects enhances young readers' observational ability, while the engaging story and hilarious dialogue develop their reading comprehension.

From Eli's hapless attempts to solve the mystery, to the fun Search & Find® activities on every page, *Eli the Spy, Where Am I?* will provide hours of fun for your little ones!

Find Eli in the Cheez-E Diner!

It's a dark and rainy night in Hollywood. Eli the Spy spots a strange-looking group of characters at the diner. "I'd better take a look," he says.

Search & Find®

Bear	Knight in armor
Bowling ball	Leaf
Dinosaur	Parrot
Dog	Pirate
Ear of corn	Raccoon hat
Elf	Sailor hat
Eye patch	Shark
Ghost	Skeleton
Guitar	Slice of watermelon
Jack-o'-lantern	Snake
King	Wristwatch

Read & Find™

1. What does the king offer for a hamburger?

2. Who is hankering for some grits?

3. What flavor is the ice-cream soda?

4. Who is afraid of rusting?

5. What does the apple want to eat?

Find Eli in the Middle Ages!

Eli leaves the diner through the back door and sees two knights on horseback. A king and queen watch them joust. How strange! Next, he checks out the castle.

Search & Find®

Axe	Jack-o'-lantern
Bird	Kite
Clothespin	Mouse
Crutch	Pig
Donkey	Pot
Dragon	Propeller
Duck	Queen
Fan	Rose
Fish	Sergeant's stripes
Helmet with horns	Tombstone
Ice-cream cone	UFO

Read & Find™

1. Who always gets the best seat?

2. What does the jousting knight's shield say?

3. Where is the man with a pot on his head supposed to be?

4. Who likes to horse around?

5. What else does the hot dog man sell?

Find Eli in Cartoonland!

Eli enters the castle and finds cartoon characters acting silly all around him. He's confused, but Eli must find out what's going on in this crazy place.

Search & Find®

Beehive	Owl
Broom	Paintbrush
Bursting balloon	Pie
Chicken	Pirate hat
Crow	Rabbit
Firefighter	Sandwich
Ghost	Saxophone
Gingerbread man	Snake
Golf tee	Swiss cheese
Grumpy elf	Toaster
Mushroom	Underwear

Read & Find™

1. Which cartoon character tears the page?

2. What is the TV delivery man about to step on?

3. Who claims that he is not the ump?

4. Why is the horse pulling a car?

5. What does the horse need?

Find Eli in the Pirates' Battle!

Eli slips through a hole in the wall and hears, "Ahoy mates!" He sees a big ship and pirates fighting with swords. It's very dangerous here!

Search & Find®

Banana peel	Milk carton
Basket	Moon
Chicken	Paper hat
Dog	Peanuts seller
Dollar sign	Piano
Fire hydrant	Pointed hat
Football	Rabbit
Hot dog	Sailboat
Jack-o'-lantern	Shovel
Ladder	Star
Mask	Watering can

Read & Find™

1. What is the name of the town's inn?

2. Why is the man looking in the mirror?

3. Where can you find a guitar?

4. Why is the boy playing the piano?

5. What is the name of the pirate ship?

Find Eli in the Future World!

Soon, blips, beeps, and wacky creatures replace the fighting pirates. Everyone is in a hurry. Eli searches for clues and heads for the space exit.

Search & Find®

Apple	Ice-cream cone
Cactus	Ice skate
Ear	Key
Elephant	Mailbox
Evergreen tree	Nail
Fish	Owl
Football	Parachute
Football helmet	Pocket watch
Fork	Postage stamp
Graduate's hat	Roller skate
Guitar	Santa Claus

Read & Find™

1. What is the witch flying on?
2. Which city is the apple going to see?
3. Who says that he is late?
4. Why can't the UFO in section E3 fly?
5. What does the alien with the food cart sell?

Find Eli in France!

The space exit leads Eli right into the middle of the French Revolution over 200 years ago. "Is that Napoleon?" he wonders. Poor Eli doesn't have a clue.

Search & Find®

Alien	French bread
Arrow	Garbage can
Ballerina	Haystack
Basket	Key
Baton twirler	Mask
Bear	Mermaid
Bowling ball	Mouse
Cardboard box	Net
Crown	Paintbrush
Firecracker	Red bird
Fishing pole	Tin can

Read & Find™

1. What is for sale in the castle?
2. Who is the pointy-eared space man talking to?
3. Where is the giant ape heading?
4. What does the unicorn want the baker to hand over?
5. Who is Tarzan looking for?

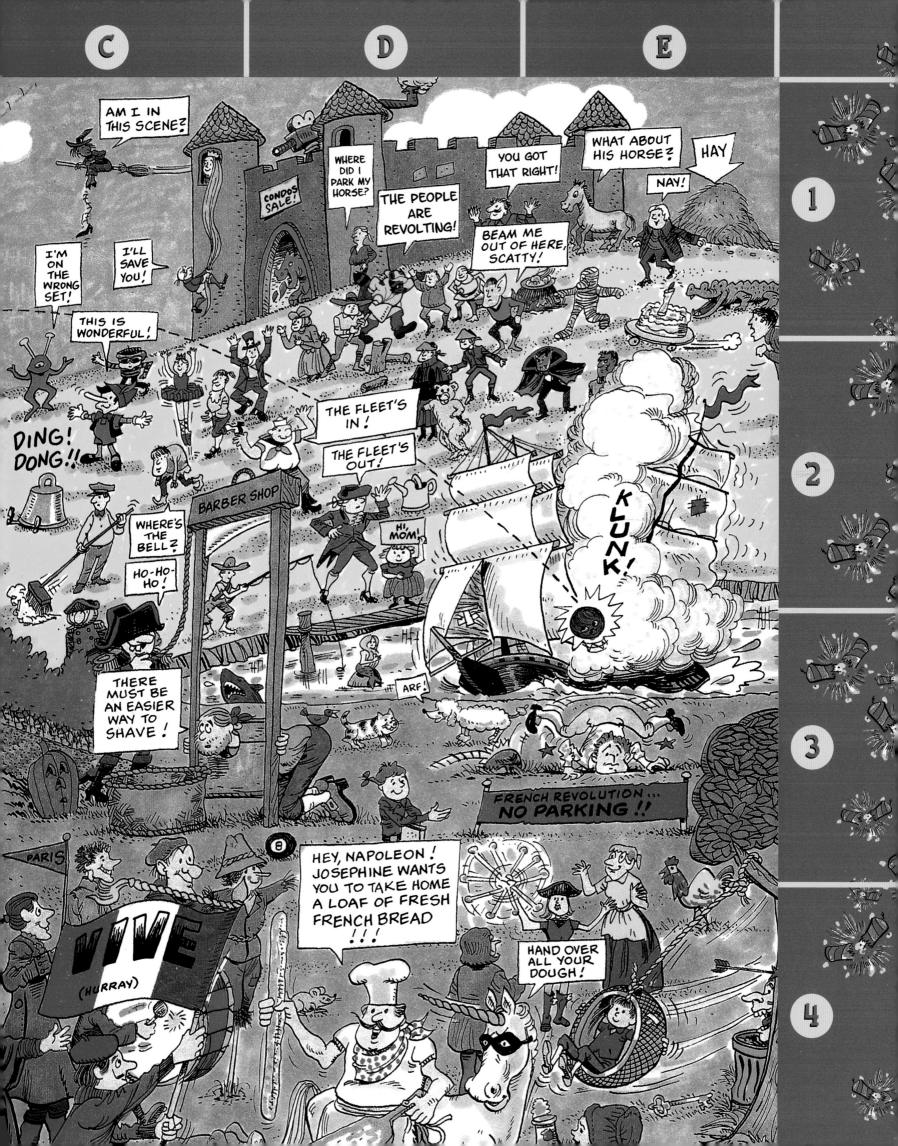

Find Eli at Fort Knocks!

What's going on here? Soldiers are running all over the place. A movie camera catches Eli's eye. "Haven't I seen one of those somewhere before?" he wonders.

Search & Find®

Alligator	Map
Baseball cap	Monster
Candle	Movie camera
Cheese	Mug
Clown	Parachute
Cow skull	Pie
Dog	Policeman
Dragon	Shark
Fire hydrant	Tank
"Jump Zone"	Target
Kite	Volcano

Read & Find™

1. What is the soldier in the tank selling?

2. Where is Robin Hood shooting arrows?

3. Which town has lots of broken windows?

4. How much is the lemonade?

5. What is wrapped around the Jungle-Land sign?

Find Eli in Italy!

Romeo and Juliet are in love. And that's not the only weird thing going on. "I will solve this case if it takes me all night!" says Eli. "Is that a lion I hear?"

Search & Find®

Baseball cap	Light bulb
Bird	Paper airplane
Candy cane	Pie
Duck	Pillow
Fishing pole	Propeller
Football player	Roller skates
Frog	Saw
Hamburger	Skateboard
Hot dog	Sock
Ice skates	Sunglasses
Key	TV set

Read & Find™

1. What does the man on ice skates think Romeo should get?

2. Who made a wrong turn?

3. Why is Juliet's brother teasing her?

4. What does the license plate on the car say?

5. When does the napping boy want to wake up?

   A   **B**

Find Eli in
Ancient Rome!

The trail leads Eli to the Roman Coliseum. But it isn't a ruin! It's full of cheering Romans. Our super spy is super scared and runs for the door.

Search & Find®

Arrow	Painted egg
Backwards helmet	Pig
Balloon	Pizza box
Banana peel	Rabbit
Cat	Shield
Emperor	Skull
Falling rock	Slice of pizza
Flower	Snake
Jack-o'-lantern	Soccer ball
Lunchbox	Star
Mask	Tire

Read & Find™

1. Where is the Tin Man going?
2. Who got in without paying?
3. What is the name of the cat's cousin?
4. Where is the secret door?
5. Who is singing about lasagna?

Find Eli in the New World!

That was close! Eli is now standing on a beach with Christopher Columbus! "Where am I?" he wonders. By now he's not surprised to be in such an odd place.

Search & Find®

Book	Ice skates
Bucket	Kite
Camera	Life preserver
Clothespin	Lizard
Clown	Lost mitten
Dog	Mermaid
Duck	Pencil
Feather	Scarecrow
Fire hydrant	Seesaw
Football	Snail
Ghost	Train

Read & Find™

1. What is Christopher Columbus' rank?

2. How far did the sailors travel on the ocean?

3. Who wants to have a cracker?

4. When was the bearded man's last bath?

5. What does the red sign say?

Find Eli in Prehistoric Times!

Eli ducks behind a palm tree into the path of a charging woolly mammoth! He sees another camera and thinks he's figured out what's going on.

Search & Find®

Balloon
Briefcase
Broom
Car
Cave
Crown
Football
Glass pitcher
Guitar
Kite
Lasso

Lion
Lunchbox
Pig
Pink flamingo
Soccer ball
Spoon
Superhero
Tin man
Tire
Trumpet
Witch

Read & Find™

1. What does the caveman sit on to rest?
2. How much does the woolly mammoth ride cost?
3. What is the name of the band?
4. Who forgot to buy film?
5. What is "out of order"?

A   B

Find Eli at the Academy Awards!

Eli pokes his head through a curtain and is handed an award! As he suspected, he had walked through 11 different movie sets! It's all in a day's work for Eli the Spy.

Search & Find®

Bat	Rabbit
Cup	Rat
Dog	Red beret
Eye patch	Saw
Fish	Sleeping man
George Washington	Soldier
Handkerchief	Spear
Medal	Spoon
Mouse	Target
Mushroom	Vampire
Painted egg	Wooden leg

Read & Find™

1. How many films did Eli star in by accident?

2. Who can't see?

3. Where does the alien want to banish Eli to?

4. Who gave the pirate a hotfoot?

5. How many feet of film did Eli ruin?

Eli in the Cheez-E Diner!

Bear	B3
Bowling ball	D4
Dinosaur	B2
Dog	C1
Ear of corn	C4
Elf	E4
Eye patch	B2
Ghost	C3
Guitar	E3
Jack-o'-lantern	C2
King	E4
Knight in armor	A3
Leaf	D4
Parrot	C3
Pirate	B2
Raccoon hat	A2
Sailor hat	A2
Shark	D2
Skeleton	A2
Slice of watermelon	B3
Snake	A4
Wristwatch	D4

Read & Find™

1. His kingdom (E4)
2. The cowboy (B3)
3. Spinach (D1)
4. The knight (A3)
5. Apple pie (D4)

Eli in the Middle Ages!

Search & Find®

Axe	D4
Bird	A4
Clothespin	B3
Crutch	A4
Donkey	E2
Dragon	E2
Duck	B1
Fan	E3
Fish	A4
Helmet with horns	C4
Ice-cream cone	B4
Jack-o'-lantern	E1
Kite	D1
Mouse	C3
Pig	E4
Pot	C3
Propeller	D3
Queen	E2
Rose	A4
Sergeant's stripes	C2
Tombstone	A3
UFO	D1

Read & Find™

1. The king (E2)
2. "Eat at Joe's" (B2)
3. The kitchen (C3)
4. Knights (C3)
5. Soda and popcorn (C4)

Eli in Cartoonland!

Search & Find®

Beehive	A2
Broom	D2
Bursting balloon	D4
Chicken	E2
Crow	B1
Firefighter	D4
Ghost	B4
Gingerbread man	A1
Golf tee	B2
Grumpy elf	B2
Mushroom	E2
Owl	D4
Paintbrush	D3
Pie	C1
Pirate hat	D2
Rabbit	A4
Sandwich	C3
Saxophone	D3
Snake	E2
Swiss cheese	C3
Toaster	C4
Underwear	C1

Read & Find™

1. Super Dude (A1)
2. A bar of soap (A2)
3. The gray elephant (D2)
4. To save gas (A3)
5. More oats (A3)

Eli in the Pirates' Battle!

Search & Find®

Banana peel	B2
Basket	C1
Chicken	E4
Dog	A2
Dollar sign	D1
Fire hydrant	E3
Football	E3
Hot dog	A3
Jack-o'-lantern	A4
Ladder	C1
Mask	B4
Milk carton	D4
Moon	B1
Paper hat	D2
Peanuts seller	A4
Piano	E4
Pointed hat	E4
Rabbit	A4
Sailboat	E4
Shovel	E2
Star	E2
Watering can	E2

Read & Find™

1. Out Inn (D1)
2. To check his wig (C2)
3. Ye dump site (E3)
4. To practice (D4)
5. SS Trouble (A3)

Eli in the Future World!

Search & Find®

Apple	E4
Cactus	D3
Ear	B3
Elephant	A2
Evergreen tree	C1
Fish	A3
Football	D1
Football helmet	E3
Fork	E2
Graduate's hat	D2
Guitar	C2
Ice-cream cone	C1
Ice skate	D4
Key	E2
Mailbox	A1
Nail	D3
Owl	B1
Parachute	D3
Pocket watch	C2
Postage stamp	A2
Roller skate	A1
Santa Claus	D4

Read & Find™

1. A jet broom (E3)
2. New York (E4)
3. The pocket watch (C2)
4. It's out of gas (E3)
5. Space subs (A4)

Eli in France!

Search & Find®

Alien	C2
Arrow	E4
Ballerina	C2
Basket	C3
Baton twirler	E4
Bear	D2
Bowling ball	E3
Cardboard box	B3
Crown	C1
Firecracker	A1
Fishing pole	D2
French bread	D4
Garbage can	E4
Haystack	E1
Key	E4
Mask	D4
Mermaid	D3
Mouse	D4
Net	A3
Paintbrush	A2
Red bird	D3
Tin can	E4

Read & Find™

1. Condos (D1)
2. Scatty (D1)
3. The Empire State Building (A1)
4. All his dough (E4)
5. Jane (B1)